D1642233

IRON MAN
LEVI PIM

ANNUAL 2009

*"**WELCOME** to Stark Industries, friend. I'm Iron Man. You're about to access the Stark Industries data-files. I'll be your guide, and may even need your help at times if any action kicks off. But remember, all you're about to read is top secret, so make sure you're not being watched... Good luck!"*

INSIDE

❋ SECRET MISSION ❋

Someone is trying to hack into my data-files and I need **YOUR** help to stop them! Look closely through the annual, and tick when you find...

6 HACKER BUGS ☐

6 VIRAL CODES ☐

Now find **10** hidden letters and rearrange below to find the name of the hacker!

☐☐☐☐ ☐☐☐☐☐☐

IRON MAN Annual 2009 is published by Panini Publishing, a division of Panini UK Limited. Editorial: Ed Caruana, Design: Will Lucas. Office of publication: Panini House, Coach and Horses Passage, The Pantiles, Tunbridge Wells, Kent TN2 5UJ. Iron Man, the Movie © 2008 MVL Film Finance LLC. Marvel, Iron Man, all character names and their distinctive likenesses: TM & © 2008 Marvel Entertainment, Inc. and its subsidiaries. All rights reserved. Super Hero(es) is a co-owned registered trademark. This publication may not be sold, except by authorised dealers, and is sold subject to the condition that it shall not be sold or distributed with any part of its cover or markings removed, nor in a mutilated condition. This publication is produced under licence from Marvel Characters, Inc. through Panini S.p.A. Printed in Italy.
ISBN: 978-1-84653-061-6

I AM IRON MAN!

BEHIND EVERY LEGEND THERE'S A TRUTH. BEHIND EVERY SUPER-HERO THERE'S A MAN. AND BEHIND IRON MAN... THERE'S TONY STARK. THIS IS HIS STORY...

THE BEGINNING!

The brilliant son of legendary weapons developer, Howard Stark, Tony Stark graduated with a double masters in Physics and Engineering from MIT at the age of nineteen. After both his parents died in a car crash, the mantle was passed on, and Tony found himself Chief Executive Officer of Stark Industries at the young age of twenty-one.

KIDNAPPED!

Following in his father's footsteps, Tony put Stark Industries at the top of the industrial ladder, with monumental breakthroughs in smart-weapons, advanced robotics and satellite targeting. But this drew the attention of many terrorist cells, and while performing a weapons test overseas Stark was ambushed, taken captive and badly injured by one of his own Stark Industries mines!

MERCHANT OF DEATH:

Held by a terror cell called the 'Followers of the Ten Rings', Tony was ordered to build his captors a devastating 'Jericho' missile in only 24 hours. Instead, Tony used his ingenuity, as well as the aid of fellow captive, Yinsen, to build a high-tech suit of armour to help them escape...

MARK 1 ARMOUR:

Trapped inside a heavily guarded cave-complex, and fighting a crippling heart condition acquired during the ambush, Stark created a miniature Repulsor reactor to keep deeply-embedded shards of metal from the Stark mine from entering his heart. He then designed his Mark 1 battle-suit to run off this revolutionary, centralised power source.

STARK FACTS:

Stark has created several other models of the armour, including suits designed for deep-sea diving, stealth and space travel, as well as a super-tough model known as the "Hulkbuster" for fighting the Hulk!

STARK FACTS:

Iron Man can also fire pulse bolts that get more powerful the further they travel, making running away from Iron Man even more dangerous than facing him!

EVOLUTION:

Upon his arrival home in the United States, after having witnessed the danger that his weapons posed to the world, Stark decided that he would no longer build weapons. But when he later stumbled upon an evil criminal plot with terrifying global implications, Stark refined the Mark 1 design, donned his powerful armour once again, and vowed to protect the world as Iron Man from the weapons his company had created!

MISSION BRIEF...
OPERATION ALPHA!

"We have a level three security breach at Stark Industries HQ! An international super-spy calling himself Spymaster has broken into my secret underground armour workshop! Before you turn the page, read these character profiles so you know who we'll be dealing with..."

SPYMASTER:

A spy for hire, Spymaster will work for anyone, anywhere - as long as the money's good. He's a gifted thief, computer hacker and all-round dirty trickster. The question is, who is he working for this time? And why? Smells like an inside job to me.

JUSTIN HAMMER:

Ruthless businessman and head of one of my biggest rivals, Hammertronics, I've never fully trusted Hammer. Trouble is, he's on the Stark Industries board of directors, so I've gotta watch my tongue. Keep an eye on this guy...

JIM RHODES:

Hot-shot pilot and closest friend, Jim's backed me up on countless missions over the years. You can always rely on Rhodey to help us out in a tight spot.

YOUR MISSION
Pay close attention during the action because I'll need your help to record all the facts for my data-files in a mission De-Brief! OK, go to the next page to begin...

STARK INTERNATIONAL CORPORATE
HEADQUARTERS, NEW YORK CITY,
SUB-BASEMENT FOUR:

CONTINUED ON PAGE 20

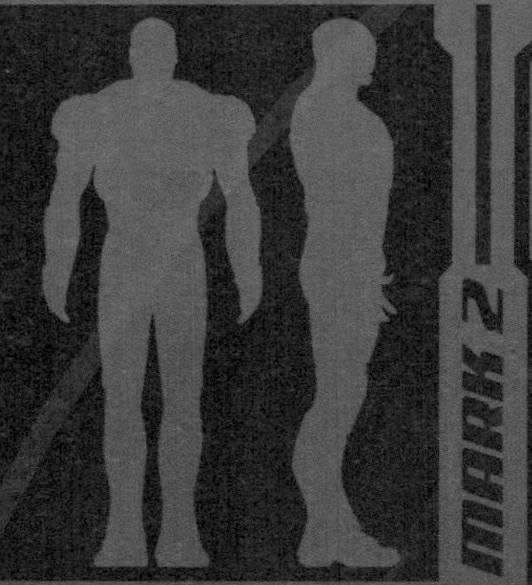

STARK INDUSTRIES

MARK 2

As Stark's enemies have evolved over the years, so has his armour. For the first time ever he's allowing you, his trusted ally, to see his ultra secret Mark 2 armour blueprints!

TACTICAL DATA DISPLAY

All critical information like fuel levels, altitude, and incoming threats are displayed on an LCD screen built into each eye.

COMMS COMPUTER

ENERGY CONVERTER

This allows the suit to absorb energy from nearby sources such as heat and electricity.

AUXILIARY BATTERIES

VOICE CONVERTOR

CYBERNETIC INTERFACE

A cerebral converter that allows the armour to be controlled by Stark's brain patterns.

SHIELD GENERATOR

STARK FACTS:

A rival of Stark's called Obadiah Stane once got hold of some of the armour blueprints and created his own model known as Iron Monger!

STARK FACTS:

Stark's cover story is that Iron Man is actually his personal bodyguard, and Stark Industries' company mascot. No-one suspects they are the same person!

SOLAR PANELS

MAGNETISED IRON SHELL

The armour itself is a super-flexible but almost unbreakable matrix of aligned iron particles, enhanced by magnetic fields over layers of other metals like titanium.

SHOCK ABSORBERS

JET THRUSTERS

Experimental super-sonic jet thrusters give Stark a top flight speed of around mach 2.1, or 1680 mph.

UNI-BEAM PROJECTOR

A powerful particle beam emitter - less accurate than the repulsor rays in the hands, but 5 times more destructive!

GAUNTLET REPULSOR RAY

Each hand has a highly accurate repulsor ray built into it, firing super-charged electron beams capable of liquifying most metals.

STARK FACTS:

Stark once lent the armour to buddy Jim Rhodes when he needed a break from action during a time of personal crisis.

JET SKATES

When Stark needs to move quickly on land, retractable skates emerge from the feet. By rotating the jet thrusters 90 degrees to the rear, he can reach land-speeds of up to 300 mph!

19

...'CAUSE STARK INTERNATIONAL'S STOCK PRICE JUST HIT THIRTY BUCKS A SHARE!
THAT'S THE MAGIC NUMBER! YOU'VE DONE ALL WE NEEDED YOU TO.
AND WE CAN'T HAVE YOU STICK AROUND TO TELL YOUR SIDE OF THE STORY, NOW CAN WE?
"WE," HUH? WHO ELSE IS IN ON THIS SCHEME OTHER THAN YOU, SPYMASTER? WHO ARE YOU WORKING FOR?
SORRY, RUSTY-- YOU DON'T CLIMB TO THE TOP OF THE CORPORATE ESPIONAGE FOOD CHAIN BY KISSING AND TELLING!
EVEN TO SOON-TO-BE STAINS ON THE SIDEWALK!
KRUNCH

briiiiing

⸽SOB⸽

HEY, MAVIS, IT'S *ME*, PEPPER--CAN YOU *TALK* FOR A MINUTE... EXECUTIVE ADMIN TO EXECUTIVE ADMIN?

OH, PEPPER...I'VE NEVER ENVIED YOU *MORE!* YOU GET TO WORK FOR A RICH, HANDSOME *GENIUS* LIKE TONY STARK... AND *I'M* STUCK WITH *JUSTIN HAMMER!*

I DON'T KNOW HOW MUCH LONGER I CAN JUST *SIT* HERE AND TAKE THAT OLD GOAT'S *ABUSE!*

...JUST JOINING US, IRON MAN IS ON AN APPARENT RAMPAGE...

WELL...YOU MAY NOT HAVE TO ENVY ME MUCH *LONGER*, MAVE. I DON'T THINK I'LL HAVE A *JOB* BY THE END OF THE DAY!

OUR HEAD OF SECURITY IS SINGLE-HANDEDLY LAYING WASTE TO NEW YORK CITY-- PRETTY SOON OUR STOCK IS GOING TO COST LESS THAN A *PACK OF GUM!*

OH, THAT *REMINDS* ME--MR. HAMMER WANTED ME TO BUY UP S.I. ONCE IT HIT THIRTY BUCKS A SHARE--I'D BETTER *GET* ON THAT, OR BOY, AM I GONNA *HEAR* IT--

WAIT! *WHAT?* HE SAID THAT? NO *WONDER* HE LOOKS SO *PLEASED* WITH HIMSELF...

DON'T *DO* IT, MAVIS! NOT UNTIL WE TALK TO *MY* BOSS!

DON'T WORRY ABOUT THAT WITHERED OLD *JERK*, HAMMER! YOU *KNOW* MR. STARK WOULD GIVE YOU A JOB *WHENEVER* YOU ASKED!

YOU DON'T *HAVE* TO PUT UP WITH HAMMER ANYMORE!

YOU'RE *RIGHT!* I'M GOING TO STAND *UP* FOR MYSELF FOR ONCE!

I AM *SECRETARY!* HEAR ME *ROAR!*

POP FIZZ

MISSION DE-BRIEF...

Whoa, that was intense! OK, after each mission I enter all the key facts into my mission data-files. But things happened so fast there's a few details I'm a little hazy on. Can you help? Tick each correct answer.

Q1 Which one of these board members was the traitor?

A. Marv Wiseman ☐

B. Justin Hammer ☐

C. Leonard Grimes ☐

Q2 What did Spymaster plant in my armour's computer console?

A. A tracker device ☐

B. A self destruct bug ☐   **C.** A remote control chip ☐

Q3 Which one of these was Spymaster's REAL override code?

A. Bacon Cheeseburger! ☐

B. Pork Chop Sandwiches! ☐

C. Macaroni Cheese! ☐

Q4 Damage to my security systems has interfered with this crimescene photo. Can you spot four things that aren't right?

Q5 What is Spymaster's real name?   **A.** Nick Shadow ☐

B. Justin Hammer ☐   **C.** Neither - we never found out ☐

31

"Welcome friend. Thanks for your back-up on Operation Alpha. Trusted allies are few and far between these days. Prove yourself on these training missions and I may just call on you again one day..."

1. NAVIGATION SKILLS

Find the correct path through this maze, copying the letters you find on the way into the code-box. ONLY the letters on the CORRECT path will spell the codeword.

START

FINISH

CODEWORD

2. MAYDAY MAYDAY!

In emergencies, I may need to send you an urgent message. This is always scrambled to stop enemies listening in. Can you put this message in the right order?

THE RAMPAGE AND MONGER IS ON BACK-UP! I NEED URGENT MAN! IRON THIS IS IRON

ENTER MESSAGE HERE

SIDEKICK!

3. CODE BREAKER

Enemy computer systems are often locked by security grids. Hack into this computer by finding and crossing out all the words.

GOLD
STARK
MONGER
TONY

RAY
ARMOUR
ENEMY
RED

```
I S T A R K
M N O D E A
O U N S D R
N T Y R I M
G O L D E O
E N E M Y U
R S R A Y R
```

GENIUS TEST!
Once you've crossed out all the words, enter the left-over letters in order into this box to complete the phrase.

STARK ☐☐☐☐☐☐☐☐☐☐☐

4. INTRUDER ALERT!

Enemies are always trying to trick their way into my Stark Industries building using fake passcards. Here's a REAL passcard, the four below are fakes. Can you spot what's wrong with each one?

VALID

STARK INDUSTRIES
LEVEL 6

(A) STARK INDUSTRIES LEVEL 6

(B) STARK INDUSTRIES LEVEL 6

(C) STARK INDUSTRIES LEVEL 6

(D) STARK INDUSTRIES LEVEL 6

MISSION COMPLETE!
If you completed all four missions correctly, welcome to the team! Turn to page 62 to check your answers!

33

IRON MONGER!

REVERSE-ENGINEERED FROM PIECES OF THE ORIGINAL MARK 1 ARMOUR, THE IRON MONGER IS AN ADVANCED PROTOTYPE INTENDED TO BE THE FIRST OF A WHOLE ARMY OF IRON SOLDIERS. IRON MAN HAS FEW DEADLIER ENEMIES...

ORIGINS:

A top executive at Stark Industries, Obadiah Stane is a cold, calculating genius who is willing to do whatever it takes to get the job done. Stane has been with Stark Industries since before Tony's birth, acting as an advisor to Tony's father, Howard. Envious of Stark's company mascot, Iron Man, but unable to match Stark's genius for inventing, Stane created his own battle-suit from stolen components of the Mark 1 armour. He called it Iron Monger.

SKULL CRUSHER GAUNTLETS

MARK 1 IRON SHELL

The shell uses the same technology as the Iron Man armour, though with a slightly heavier and less complex iron particle matrix. This gives Iron Monger less freedom of movement, though a greater protection against impacts.

SPEC:

Based on the Mark 1 armour specs, it lacks the complexity of the later Iron Man models. However, due to its simplistic design, it is able to focus a greater extent of power on good, old-fashioned brute force!

PSYCH PROFILE:

Driven by an intense desire to succeed, Stane will take out anything or anyone that stands between him and his goals. By always keeping his enemies close, he knows exactly where to hit them when he needs them out of the picture!

H.U.D. DISPLAY

Through the Iron Monger's Heads Up Display (HUD), the wearer can analyze the battlefield in a variety of settings, including infra-red, thermal, night-vision and x-ray.

WEAPON SYSTEMS

As well as repulsor rays in each hand-gauntlet, Iron Monger is equipped with a mounted, high-velocity mini-gun capable of spraying over 100 bullets per second!

UNI-BEAM PROJECTOR

SPRING-LOADED KNEE JOINTS

HYDRAULICS

Powerful hydraulics in Iron Monger's legs allow it to leap great distances and crush anything in its path!

MAGNETISED FOOT PLATES

≪ HEAD TO HEAD ≫

	STRENGTH	
9		9
	WEAPONS	
8		9
	SPEED	
9		8
	FLEXIBILITY	
9		7

MISSION BRIEF...
OPERATION DELTA!

"For years I've been searching for a new source of energy to replace fast-depleting fossil fuels. Finally I think I've found one - the only trouble is, it's buried beneath the sea-bed smack in the centre of the Bermuda Triangle! I'll need your help again to record all my findings after the mission, so be alert. Here's the lowdown before we begin..."

COMMANDER KRAKEN:

Sailors that have ventured these waters and survived have reported sightings of strange submarine-sized creatures beneath the waves. The word is a deranged pirate calling himself Commander Kraken leads a crew of highly advanced techno-pirates, and pilots some kind of mechanical sea-monster. But if you ask me, it's just too much sea air getting to sailor's brains!

THE BERMUDA TRIANGLE:

The so called 'Bermuda Triangle' is a patch of ocean in which countless sea and air-craft have disappeared without a trace. No-one has ever been able to explain why - maybe I'll find some answers during the mission...

YOUR MISSION
Just like Operation Alpha, you're my eyes and ears. When the mission's over, head to the De-Brief section to update my mission files. OK, let's move

THE BERMUDA TRIANGLE:
SEDIMENT VELOCITY: HIGH
ELECTRICAL RESISTIVITY: LOW
CHANCE OF LOCATING GAS HYDRATE: 0%
Another dead end...

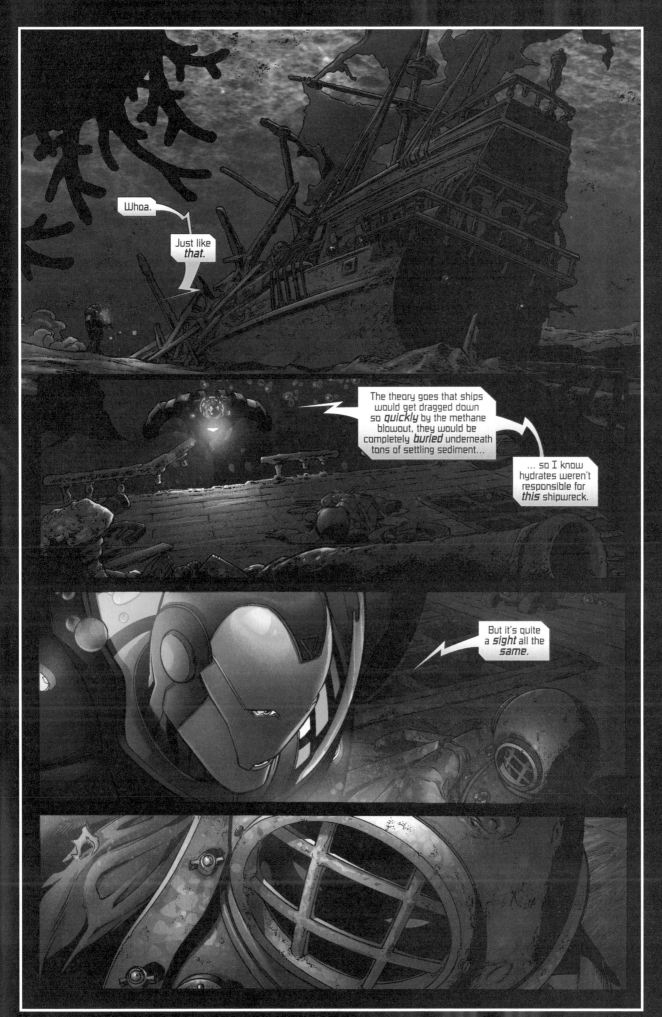

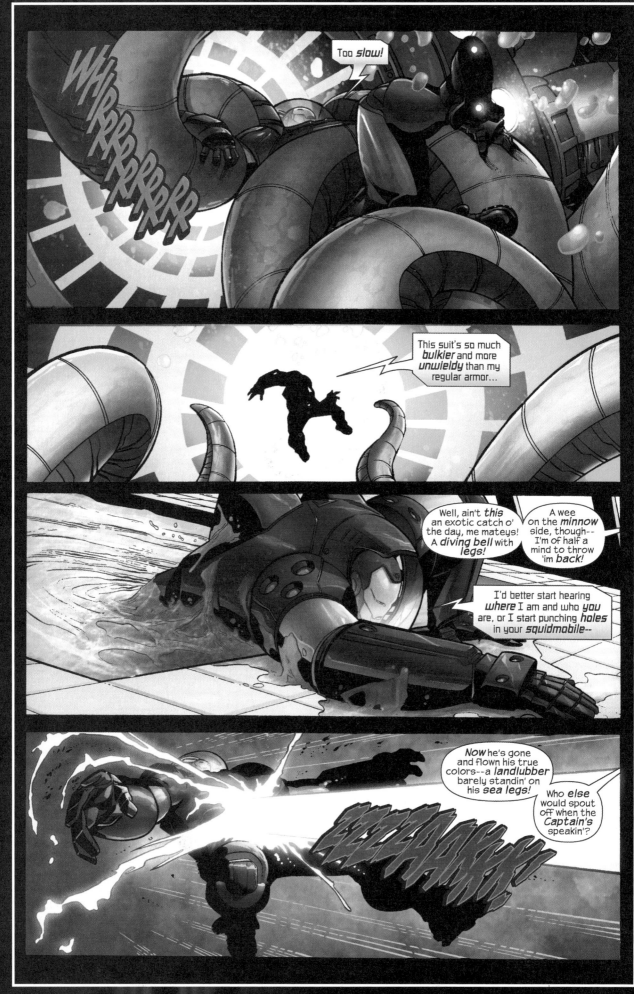

STARK INDUSTRIES

MARK 1

THE MARK 1 ARMOUR MAY NOT BE PRETTY, BUT IT GETS THE JOB DONE. BUT BUILT SOLELY FOR STARK'S PROTECTION DURING HIS ESCAPE FROM CAPTIVITY, WINNING A FASHION CONTEST WAS THE LAST THING ON HIS MIND! HERE'S HOW HE DID IT...

REPULSOR

A mine blast during his capture left Stark with a life-threatening heart condition. This Repulsor reactor stops the shards of metal from the mine from entering his heart.

STEEL-MESH GAUNTLETS

To protect Stark's hands from the intense heat of the flame-throwers, the gloves were made from a multi-weaved iron chainmail.

BULLET-PROOF IRON HELM

IRON SHELL

When constructing the armour, Stark and Yinsen knew it needed to withstand sustained, full-frontal attacks. That's why they focused most of their efforts on creating a bullet-proof, missile-proof exterior!

PROPANE TANK

SECONDARY FLAME-THROWER

HYDRAULICS

Super-high pressure pistons fitted throughout the armour's hinge joints turn the arms, legs, feet and fists into virtual battering rams - ideal for smashing through walls, doors and ranks of enemy soldiers!

IRON MAN   MARK 1

ORIGINAL PLANS

Having to keep the work on the Mark 1 undercover, separate sketches were created with only certain pieces of the armour on each. Only when brought together are the armour's full specs revealed.

REPULSION BOOTS

FLAME-THROWER

Using a propane tank stolen from the terrorists, the flame-thrower proved to be the most effective weapon against his oncoming captors. Fuel is pumped from the tank through the orange pipe and is ignited by a spark from the pipe beside it.

POWER TREAD

The movement of each leg joint is powered by a motorised chain belt, providing Stark with the leg strength to support the massive weight of the armour.

47

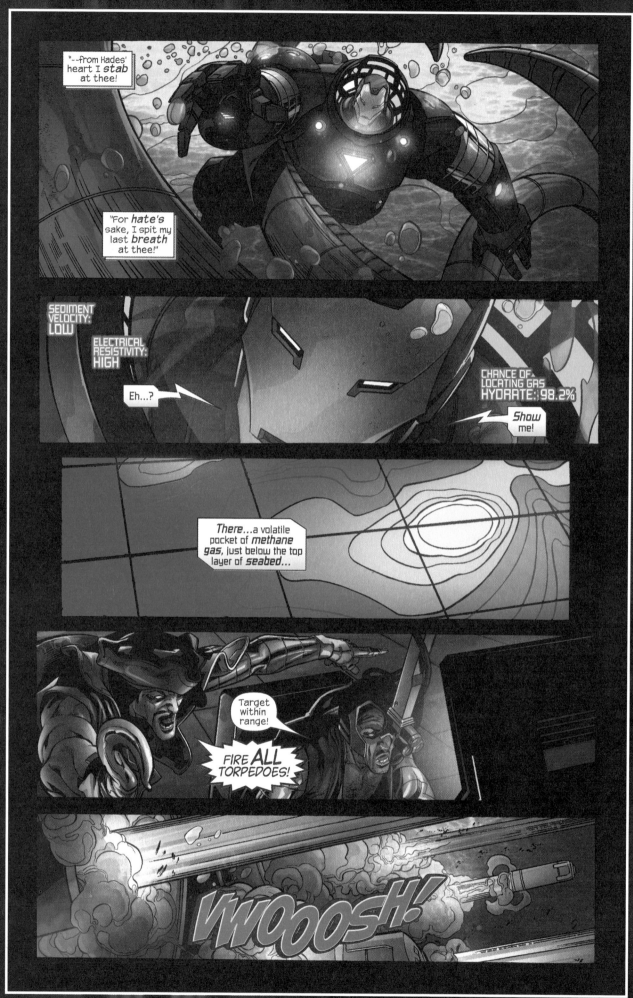

HOURS LATER:

AREA SCAN: NEGATIVE

Incredible...I can't find a *trace* of Commander Kraken or his sub *anywhere!*

Like so many *others*, they've been *swallowed up* by the *Bermuda Triangle!*

THE END

MISSION DE-BRIEF...

Well that was weird! Commander Kraken?! Commander Krack-Pot more like! OK, you know the drill. I need your help again to complete my mission records. Were you paying attention? Time to find out!

Q1| What was Commmander Kraken before his pirate days?

A. A Naval Officer

B. A scientist

C. A computer hacker

Q2| What was the facility called that Kraken attacked?

A. Aqualab

B. Waterworld

C. Hydrobase

Q3| Kraken's old workmate called him by his real name. What was it?

A. Albert   B. Wade   C. Steve

Q4| Kraken's security system played havoc with my camera. Can you spot five changes he's made to the picture below?

Q5| Can you put these events in the correct order? Number them 1-4 in the order they happened.

Q6| Which one of these pirates used my armour chestplate?

61

Turn to page 62 to check your answers!

ANSWERS

ALPHA! DE-BRIEF

Q1 B Q2 C Q3 B

Q4

Q5 C

DELTA! DE-BRIEF

Q1 B Q2 C Q3 C

Q4

Q5

Q6

IRON SIDEKICK!

1.

CODEWORD: **IRON**

2.
"THIS IS IRON MAN! IRON MONGER IS ON THE RAMPAGE AND I NEED URGENT BACK-UP!"

3.

```
I S T A R K
M N O D E A
O U N S D R
N T V R I M
G O L D E O
E N E M Y U
R S P A Y R
```

GENUS TEST:
INDUSTRIES

4.
A: Blue number box B: Orange slider
C: Yellow title D: White card rim

* SECRET MISSION *

 HACKER BUGS ARE ON PAGES:
4, 29, 33, 35, 46 & 61

VIRAL CODES ARE ON PAGES:
6, 19, 31, 34, 36 & 54

HACKER'S NAME:
IRON MONGER!